I like my...

_____

_____

_____

_____

_____

_____

_____

1b

I like to pretend I...

_____

_____

_____

_____

_____

_____

I would like
a great big...

It's hard for me to...

On Saturdays, I like to...

_____
_____
_____
_____
_____
_____
_____
_____

I feel silly when...

_____
_____
_____
_____
_____
_____
_____
_____

I'm sure glad I...

_____

_____

_____

_____

_____

_____

CLICK!

Sometimes I'm afraid of...

_____

_____

_____

_____

_____

_____

A funny thing that happened in our family was...

_____

_____

_____

_____

_____

_____

_____

When I grow up, I...

_____

_____

_____

_____

_____

_____

_____

I'm pretty good at...

_____
_____
_____
_____
_____
_____
_____
_____
_____

I hate it when...

THUMP

_____
_____
_____
_____
_____
_____
_____
_____

At school I like to...

_____
_____
_____
_____
_____
_____
_____
_____

My family likes to...

_____
_____
_____
_____
_____
_____

I am afraid to...

_____
_____
_____
_____
_____
_____
_____
_____

I laugh when...

HA HA
HEE HEE
HOO HOO

_____
_____
_____
_____
_____
_____
_____

Two of my favorite things are...

_____

_____

_____

_____

_____

_____

_____

I don't like to...

_____

_____

_____

_____

_____

_____

_____

Once someone helped me by...

_____

_____

_____

_____

_____

_____

_____

I would hate to lose...

_____

_____

_____

_____

_____

_____

_____

_____

I love to give...

_____
_____
_____
_____
_____
_____
_____
_____
_____
_____

GOOD THING!

I'd like to say a good thing about...

_____
_____
_____
_____
_____
_____
_____

I like to play...

_____
_____
_____
_____
_____
_____
_____
_____

When people get angry, they should...

_____
_____
_____
_____
_____
_____

Something I once did all by myself is...

_____

_____

_____

_____

_____

_____

_____

_____

_____

If I could be invisible, I would...

_____

_____

_____

_____

_____

_____

_____

I was really scared once when...

_____

_____

_____

_____

_____

_____

_____

_____

I always feel good when...

_____

_____

_____

_____

_____

_____

_____

_____

I once got hurt when...

_____
_____
_____
_____
_____
_____
_____
_____

I was very happy the time that...

_____
_____
_____
_____
_____
_____

My face has a big smile when...

_____
_____
_____
_____
_____
_____
_____
_____
_____

I hate to eat...

_____
_____
_____
_____
_____
_____
_____
_____
_____

I would not like to live without...

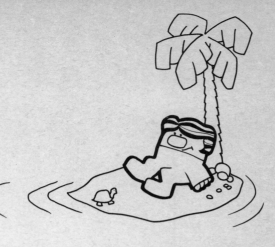

_____

_____

_____

_____

_____

_____

_____

I wish I could...

_____

_____

_____

_____

_____

_____

_____

I wish people would stop...

_____

_____

_____

_____

_____

_____

_____

I like the sound of...

_____

_____

_____

_____

_____

_____

_____

If I had a million dollars, I would...

_____
_____
_____
_____
_____
_____
_____

I feel sad when...

_____
_____
_____
_____
_____
_____
_____
_____

If I could do anything I wanted, I would...

_____
_____
_____
_____
_____
_____

I hope that...

_____
_____
_____
_____
_____
_____

I would like to learn how to...

_____

_____

_____

_____

_____

_____

_____

_____

_____

If I were a giant, I would...

_____

_____

_____

_____

_____

_____

_____

_____

_____

_____

I really like...

_____
_____
_____
_____
_____
_____
_____
_____
_____

What really bothers me is...

_____
_____
_____
_____
_____
_____

I'll never forget...

_____

_____

_____

_____

_____

_____

_____

_____

_____

I like the way I...

_____

_____

_____

_____

_____

_____

_____

_____

Two things I like about myself are...

_____

_____

_____

_____

_____

_____

_____

_____

I sometimes get mad when...

_____

_____

_____

_____

_____

_____

_____

I would not like to have...

25a

_____

_____

_____

_____

_____

_____

_____

_____

25b

I feel happiest when...

_____

_____

_____

_____

_____

_____

_____

_____

_____

If I were a bird,
I would...

_____

_____

_____

_____

_____

I feel bad when...

_____

_____

_____

_____

_____

_____

I would like a magic ring that...

_____
_____
_____
_____
_____
_____
_____
_____

School would be better if...

SUGGESTION BOX

_____
_____
_____
_____
_____
_____
_____

After I cry, I...

_____
_____
_____
_____
_____
_____
_____
_____
_____
_____

I feel important when...

_____
_____
_____
_____
_____
_____
_____
_____
_____

I would like to say something nice to...

_____

_____

_____

_____

_____

_____

_____

_____

I would be happier if...

_____

_____

_____

_____

_____

_____

_____

If I have my own children someday, I'll be sure to...

I just love...

I need more...

_____
_____
_____
_____
_____
_____
_____
_____

If I were older, I would...

_____
_____
_____
_____
_____

I would like someone to help me...

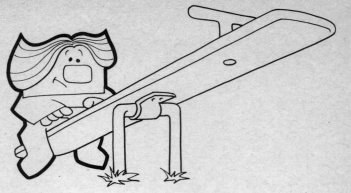

_____
_____
_____
_____
_____
_____
_____

I love to eat...

_____
_____
_____
_____
_____
_____
_____

I don't like it when...

_____
_____
_____
_____
_____
_____
_____
_____
_____
_____
_____

I am very good at...

_____
_____
_____
_____
_____
_____
_____
_____
_____
_____
_____

At night I like to...

_____
_____
_____
_____
_____
_____
_____
_____
_____

I'd use a magic wand to...

_____
_____
_____
_____
_____
_____
_____
_____

You can tell when someone likes you by...

_____
_____
_____
_____
_____
_____

If I were a teacher, I would...

_____
_____
_____
_____
_____
_____

The best time for me is when...

_____

_____

_____

_____

_____

_____

_____

If I had very long legs, I would...

_____

_____

_____

_____

_____

_____

_____

37a

I'm the kind of person who...

_____
_____
_____
_____
_____
_____
_____
_____
_____

37b

I look best when...

_____
_____
_____
_____
_____
_____
_____
_____
_____

I just love to...

_____
_____
_____
_____
_____
_____
_____
_____

I wish I could change...

_____
_____
_____
_____
_____
_____
_____

I don't like it when people...

_____
_____
_____
_____
_____
_____
_____
_____

I sometimes wonder if...

_____
_____
_____
_____
_____
_____
_____

I would like to give a present of ___ to...

_____

_____

_____

_____

_____

_____

_____

One of the best things about me is...

_____

_____

_____

_____

_____

_____

_____

When I was little...

I like going home because...

I feel happy when people...

_____

_____

_____

_____

_____

_____

_____

_____

If I were very tiny, I would...

_____

_____

_____

_____

_____

_____

_____

_____

I wish someone would give me a gift box containing...

_____
_____
_____
_____
_____
_____
_____

I felt like crying when...

_____
_____
_____
_____
_____
_____
_____

Something at home I like very much is...

_____

_____

_____

_____

_____

_____

_____

_____

I know how to...

_____

_____

_____

_____

_____

_____

_____

_____

Someday I would like to help solve the problem of...

_____
_____
_____
_____
_____

I am happiest when...

_____
_____
_____
_____
_____
_____

My family likes the way I...

_____
_____
_____
_____
_____
_____
_____
_____
_____

The best thing about school is...

_____
_____
_____
_____
_____
_____
_____

It was hard to do it, but I finally...

_____

_____

_____

_____

_____

_____

_____

_____

The best thing about a pet is...

_____

_____

_____

_____

_____

_____

After school I...

_____
_____
_____
_____
_____
_____
_____
_____
_____
_____

Some people like the way I...

_____
_____
_____
_____
_____
_____